Anan
and the Web Trick

Written by Abigail Steel

Illustrated by Marc Pattenden

RISING STARS

Anansi went to see his pal Rabbit.

I can smell carrot muffins.
Sniff!
Sniff!

You can have a muffin if you pick up plums.

I will pick up plums for you.

Then come back for a muffin!

I do not want to help.
I will trick Rabbit.

Anansi did not help Rabbit.
Anansi had fun!

Anansi spun a web.
It was a big web!

Anansi! Did you pick up the plums?

Anansi was asleep!
Rabbit had all the muffins.

Talk about the story

Ask your child these questions:

1 Whose house did Anansi go to?

2 What did Anansi smell?

3 Why do you think Anansi fell asleep?

4 Why did Rabbit get all the muffins?

5 What would you say to Anansi when he woke up?

6 Do you like helping your friends? Why or why not?

Can your child retell the story in their own words?